G000136433

An Armful of Bears

Also edited by Catherine Baker

A BRONTOSAURUS CHORUS

An Armful of Bears

Edited by Catherine Baker
Illustrated by Chris Riddell

Methuen Children's Books

This anthology first published in Great Britain 1993
by Methuen Children's Books
an imprint of Reed Children's Books Limited
Michelin House, 81 Fulham Road, London SW3 6RB
and Auckland, Melbourne, Singapore and Toronto

Copyright for this anthology © 1993 Catherine Baker
Illustrations copyright © 1993 Chris Riddell

ISBN 0 416 187382

A CIP catalogue record for this book is
available at the British Library

Typeset by Methuen Children's Books
Printed in Great Britain by St Edmundsbury Press

Contents

The Bestest Bear Song

        Oh,
     this is the
        bear,
     the very best
        bear,
     the best *bestest* best
        bear
        of all.
It's lost one leg
and it's lost one eye
and it's spotty
and it's grotty
and it's small.
        But
     this is the
        bear,
     the very best
        bear,
     the best *bestest* best
        bear
        of all.
        Yes, Sir!

It's wobbly and worn
and its left ear is torn
but it's been with me
since the day I was born
and I love,
oh, I love
its soft fur.
    For
  this is the
    bear,
  the very best
    bear,
  the best *bestest* best
    bear
    of all!
    Yes, Sir!

WES MAGEE

The Waltzing Polar Bears

While the snowy owl hoots and the
    Arctic fox wails,
The polar bear waltzes
In white tie and tails.

His top hat gets tilted as he spins
    around twice,
His long claws go rattling
Over the ice.

The Northern Lights up in the
heavens glow down
As his partner appears
In a shimmering gown.

Reflected in glaciers, they dance
jaw-to-jaw
Through the hail and the blizzard
And the hurricane's roar.

He wheels her around on her
   sparkling slippers
While the seals and penguins
Applaud with their flippers

And squawk in amazement and
   bark with delight
At the polar bears waltzing
Through the long Arctic night.

ANDREW MATTHEWS

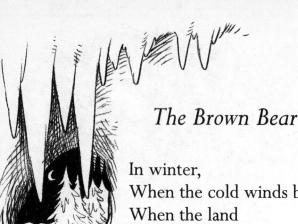

The Brown Bear

In winter,
When the cold winds blow,
When the land
Is covered with snow
The brown bear sleeps.

In winter,
When the nights come soon,
When the land
Freezes beneath the moon
The brown bear dreams.

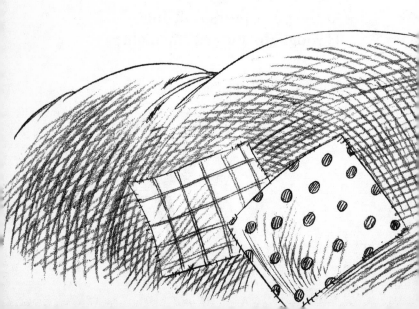

The brown bear
Dreams of summer heat,
Of berries,
Honey and nuts to eat.
The brown bear sighs.

The brown bear
Stirs, then digs down deep,
Safe and sound
In its winter sleep.
The brown bear dreams.

JOHN FOSTER

Forbears

Mr Edward Cyril Terence de Bear
(Known to his friends as 'Ted')
Is a plumpish, handsome millionaire
Who likes his breakfast in bed.
He lives in a splendid country house
With views all around of the sea
And if you ask nicely, he'll show you about
For the tiniest entrance fee.

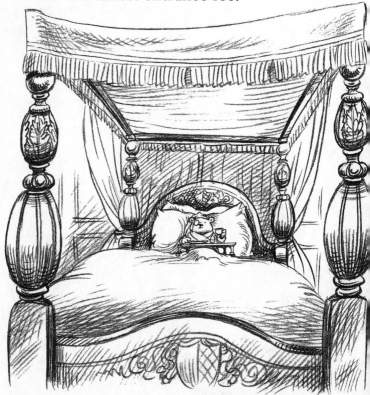

MATER & PATER

The house, which is fine, is well worth a look.
Some tables and chairs are antique.
In the cellar there's wine, in the library, a book –
Due back at the end of last week.
But the finest of all are the pictures (of bears) –
All from de Bear's Family Tree.
Gilt-framed they are hung in the hall,
 on the stairs
And everywhere else, you will see.

Mr Edward de Bear will tell you with pride
Of each portrait, exactly who's who.
There's Suzy, his sister, with Ma at her side;
By the door is Great Uncle Hugh.
There's grand-père de Bear, of foreign descent,
And his father, who joined the Dragoons.
Then Aunt May, who lived all her life in a tent,
And Jim, who loved blowing up balloons.

There are nieces and nephews and all
  sorts of cousins:
Bears bearing the family name.
Their pictures are there in their
  dozens and dozens
(All looking a little the same).
And when the tour's over, you're ready to go,
You're needing a breath of fresh air –
You'll have learnt rather more than you
  wanted to know
About Edward C. Terence de Bear.

MARK BURGESS

Honey Bear

There was a big bear
Who lived in a cave;
His greatest love
Was honey.
He had twopence a week
Which he never could save,
So he never had
Any money.
I bought him a money box
Red and round,
In which to put
His money.
He saved and saved
Till he got a pound,
Then he spent it all
On honey.

ELIZABETH LANG

The Old Person of Ware

There was an Old Person of Ware,
Who rode on the back of a bear:
When they ask'd, 'Does it trot?' –
  he said, 'Certainly not!
He's a Moppsikon Floppsikon bear!'

EDWARD LEAR

Bruin's Mistake

Bruin loved honey
And he thought he heard a bee,
So he climbed up a pole
That he took for a tree.

The buzzing got louder
As Bruin climbed higher,
But he found no bees,
Just a telephone wire!

CELIA WARREN

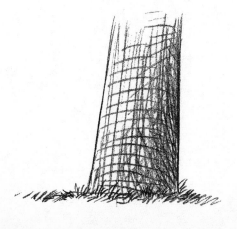

Teddy Bear Rap

I'm a big boy now
I can go to school
I can cross the road
'Cos I know the rule.
I can stay for lunch
Have packed sandwiches
I can squirt my milk
Make an awful mess.
I can do my sums
Add up three and three
I can write my name
And my A.B.C.
I'm a big boy now
Like I've just said
But I still take my teddy
When I go to bed.

MARGARET RYAN

I Can't Find My Teddy Bear!

I can't find my teddy bear,
any place, *anywhere!*

Sometimes,
he's inside Mum's sewing box,
darning and mending his woolly socks.

But not today!

Sometimes,
he can be found in our washing machine,
spinning around, trying to get clean.

But not today!

Sometimes,
he sits on top of Dad's chair,
then tumbles down as if for a dare.

But not today!

25

Sometimes,
when the weather is sunny and fine,
he swings around on the washing line.

But not today!

And sometimes,
he zooms by on a roller skate,
flashing past at such a rate!

But *definitely* not today!

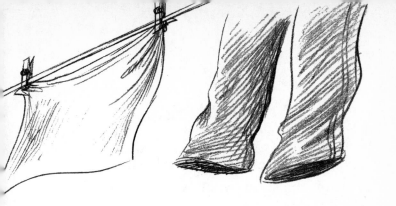

But as the day runs out of light
and the sky turns on the night,
I find him, *at last*, in the best place to be,
propped up on my bed just waiting for me!

IAN SOUTER

Teddy Bear

Teddy was under the lilac bush –
when the snow went away, we found
   him there.
And one of his shoe-button eyes was lost
and the shine was gone from his yellow hair.
But Teddy blinked with his last black eye
and said that he really didn't care
(except that his cave was a trifle cold)…
as long as we came and found him there.
And he said with a smile on his white
   yarn mouth
that REAL bears slept in a cave or lair
all through the winter…and if they could,
well then, why couldn't a TEDDY bear?

AILEEN FISHER

Bear Story

Beware the bear! The big black bear
Is prowling round somewhere out there.
He eats (they say) bad girls and boys
Who naughtily make too much noise,
Tell whopping lies or slam the door
Or tip their cabbage on the floor
Or pinch the babe to make him bawl
Or write rude words upon the wall
Or change the time on all the clocks
Or blow their noses in their socks –
So if you do those things, beware!
The bear, the bear, the big black bear
Is prowling round somewhere out there
And he will have you for his tea.
At least, that's what they say to me.

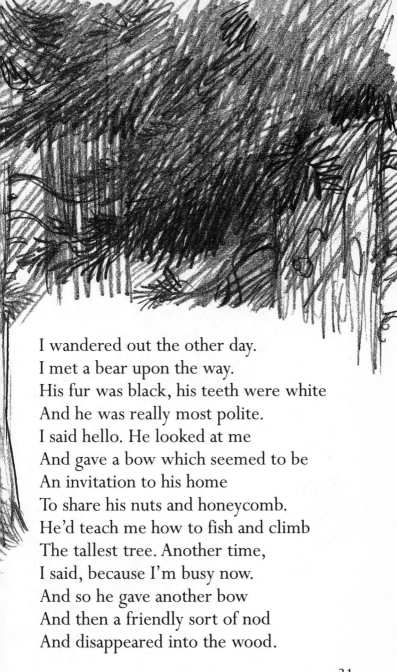

I wandered out the other day.
I met a bear upon the way.
His fur was black, his teeth were white
And he was really most polite.
I said hello. He looked at me
And gave a bow which seemed to be
An invitation to his home
To share his nuts and honeycomb.
He'd teach me how to fish and climb
The tallest tree. Another time,
I said, because I'm busy now.
And so he gave another bow
And then a friendly sort of nod
And disappeared into the wood.

31

When I got back, they made a scene.
They asked me where on earth I'd been
All afternoon. And so I told
Them who I'd met. And did they scold!
'If you tell lies like that, beware!
The bear, the bear, the big black bear –'
But I don't care.

LEON ROSSELSON

Bamboozled!

A polar bear just loves an icy landscape,
The eagle likes a mountain with a view;
A whale demands an oceanful of water...
All *I* want is a thicket of BAMBOO!

The magpie gathers sticks and straw for
   nesting,
For a woodlouse some rotting bark will do;
The rabbit digs her home beneath the
   forest...
For *mine* I just need old stalks of BAMBOO!

Some tasty mouse is buzzard's choice for
   dinner,
A field of grass is what a cow will chew;
Koalas can't resist their eucalyptus...
All *I* need is a bunch of ripe BAMBOO!

Please!

JUDITH NICHOLLS

34

Bears

Roly poly polar bears,
Rolling in the snow,
Sliding over icebergs,
In the sea they go:

Splish, splash polar bears,
Splish, splash, splosh!

Growly brown mountain bears,
Climbing on all fours,
Hugging each other
With their big brown paws:

Stump, stomp brown bears,
Stump, stomp, stamp!

CELIA WARREN

Polar Bear

The secret of the polar bear
Is that he wears long underwear.

GAIL KREDENSER

My Teddy Bear

A teddy bear is nice to hold.
The one I have is getting old.
His paws are almost wearing out
And so's his funny furry snout
From rubbing on my nose of skin,
And all his fur is pretty thin.
A ribbon and a piece of string
Make a sort of necktie thing.
His eyes came out and now instead
He has some new ones made of thread.
I take him everywhere I go
And tell him all the things I know.
I like the way he feels at night,
All snuggled up against me tight.

MARGARET HILLERT

39

Protecting Teddy

I'm holding my teddy this tight just in case
He's thrown in that washing machine.
Last time you put him there he had a fright
And he's not like *him* when he's clean.

He hates somersaulting around in that soap
And it always makes him shrink.
He'd come out some other colour, I know,
When I've just got used to him pink.

MICHELLE MAGORIAN

Big Ted

Big Ted is fun to have around,
he's a really big-hearted bear.
I've loved him ever since the day
Dad won him at the fair.

If I bump Big Ted down the stairs
he never seems to worry,
he doesn't complain or make a fuss
or tell me I'll be sorry.

The smile upon his face
never seems to disappear.
He didn't even frown or wince
when Mum re-stitched his ear.

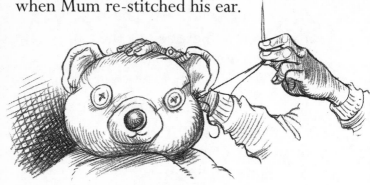

Big Ted worries about me
when I'm at school each day –
will I dress up warm enough
when I'm sent out to play?

He mothers me when Mum's not there,
he understands when I'm sad,
he's never grumpy or sharp with me
and nothing makes him mad.

I'm almost as tall as him now,
but no matter how much I grow,
Big Ted is a special friend to me
and always will be, I know.

BRIAN MOSES

Hard to Bear

'I'm very drowsy,' said the Bear;
'I think it's anything but fair
That just about the Christmas season,
Without a sign of rhyme or reason,
I get so tired I have to creep
Into a cave and fall asleep.

I take a nap, and – to my surprise –
I find, when I wake and rub my eyes,
That winter's gone, and I've slept away
Thanksgiving, Christmas and New Year's Day.

I believe that I'm not given to croaking,
But you must admit that it's provoking!'

TUDOR JENKS

A Grizzly Tale

Never trust a grizzly bear,
No matter how delightful.
You cannot take them anywhere,
Their manners are so frightful.

They prowl the woods with hungry looks
All summertime and autumn,
And steal the fish from anglers' hooks
Before they've even caught 'em.

They loll about and scratch for fleas.
They turn out dustbins nightly.
They join in people's picnic teas
And never ask politely.

They just sit down and start to cram
Their mouths with pies and chicken,
With sandwiches, with rolls and ham,
Whatever they can stick in,

And munch the lot without a pause.
Then if there's cake they grab it.
And afterwards they lick their claws –
A quite disgusting habit!

That's bad enough, but when in spring
A grizzly wakes from snoozing,
He's ready to eat anything,
And doesn't bother choosing.

Oh, then, beware the grizzly bear
For if you meet one then you
Could end up on his Bill of Fare,
A grizzly's teatime menu!

DEREK SAMPSON

Hibernation Song

I'm a Bear —
Not a polar or a grizzly but a *brown* bear.
When winter comes I hibernate away from
  wind and showers
And dream of honey, tasty fish and happy
  summer hours.
Not for me the ice-cap and all those
  frozen fish,
Nor to meet bad-tempered grizzly bears
  whose moods are devilish —
I'm a brown bear and I'm very happy
  with my way of life,
And when I wake up from my sleep,
  I'll find myself a wife.

MARK WETHERBY

51

Polar Bear

Into the shivering
water he goes.
Swift, through
the rippling green.
Then surfacing
he snorts.
Blows the water
from his nose.
Between
his needle teeth
he holds
a glittering fish.

Polar bear.
Here by his rigid
artificial pool
he shakes
the quivering drops
from his white fur
still spiked with wet.
Takes his meal
alone while
children watch.

Yet I see him there.
In the bone-white
land of bitter
drift where snow-
wolves lift their
howling voices
to the vastness
of the night.
And Polar Bear's
forgotten past.

ANN BONNER

Brown Bear Fishing

At the river's edge
the water flies,
and sprays its white
in the bear's clear eyes.

But still he watches
and prowls along,
and carefully listens
to the waterfall's song.

Like a large brown log
stood up on end,
the bear stands silent
and then he bends.

Across the screaming foam
he sweeps a paw,
and a glistening fish
is lifted on a gleaming claw.

ROBIN MELLOR

Wild Bear / Tame Bear
(Can it be the same bear?)

Bears in the bushes,
bears in the trees,
bears scoffing mice and frogs,
gobbling grass and leaves.

Bears fishing rivers,
bears killing seals,
bears on other bears
picking off fleas.

Bears in a circus,
bears wearing chains,
bears bearing blisters,
dancing in pain.

Bears bored stiff in pits,
bears begging food,
bears biting other bears,
dying in zoos.

GINA DOUTHWAITE

The Small Brown Bear

The small brown bear
fishes
with stony paws

eating ice salmon
all waterfall slippery
till his teeth ache.

MICHAEL BALDWIN

Who Am I?

I am the oldest of the bears
but I will never die!
I wander slowly, silently
beneath the midnight sky.

I am the largest of the bears;
I cannot sleep or fly,
and yet I rest above the clouds
and dance when the moon is high.

I am the farthest of the bears:
beyond the sun I lie!
I wander with a million stars…

I'm the Great Bear in the sky!

JUDITH NICHOLLS